In this stunning anthology of poems Virginia Mc[and the] acclaimed anthologist Anne Harvey look afresh at wild animals and the world in which they live. The collection is not just a celebration of the beauty and individuality of the animal world but also provides a critical look at the problems which face it: the effects on the lives of animals in captivity or performing in the circus ring; the threats of extinction and exploitation by man; the dangers of pollution in the environment.

Anne Harvey trained as an actress at the Guildhall School of Music and Drama after leaving school. She worked for some years in repertory theatre, radio and TV and then taught drama, adjudicated and examined for drama festivals and grade exams. Anne now works entirely freelance, editing poetry anthologies, running workshops and generally widening the poetry horizons of children. She directs a professional theatre company, gives poetry readings, and is an active member of the Poetry Society.

Virginia McKenna is an actress and conservationist, well known for her roles in *Born Free* and *Ring of Bright Water*. She is one of the founders of Zoo Check, a charity concerned with the welfare of animals in captivity and the conservation of their natural habitat. She is also the author of several books about wild animals.

Tessa Lovatt-Smith is a freelance artist who trained at Eastbourne and Maidstone Colleges of Art. She has a keen interest in natural history and works part time for a conservation group.

HEADLINES FROM THE JUNGLE

Edited by
Anne Harvey and Virginia McKenna

Illustrated by Tessa Lovatt-Smith

PUFFIN BOOKS

PUFFIN BOOKS

Published by the Penguin Group
Penguin Books Ltd, 27 Wrights Lane, London W8 5TZ, England
Penguin Books USA Inc., 375 Hudson Street, New York, New York 10014, USA
Penguin Books Australia Ltd, Ringwood, Victoria, Australia
Penguin Books Canada Ltd, 10 Alcorn Avenue, Toronto, Ontario, Canada L3R 1B4
Penguin Books (NZ) Ltd, 182–190 Wairau Road, Auckland 10, New Zealand

Penguin Books Ltd, Registered Offices: Harmondsworth, Middlesex, England

First published by Viking 1990
Published in Puffin Books 1991
1 3 5 7 9 10 8 6 4 2

Filmset in Monophoto Palatino

Copyright information for individual poems is given on pages 111–112
which constitute an extension of this copyright page

Printed in England by Clays Ltd, St Ives plc

CONTENTS

INTRODUCTION

Although our interest in wild animals is deeply shared, our awareness originated in very different ways. I met Anne through working with her in the theatre, doing poetry programmes together, and it is through literature and, in particular, poetry, that her fascination and her concern about their exploitation by human beings, sprang.

My interest began over a quarter of a century ago when my husband and I were in the film *Born Free* — slowly but surely the pattern of my life began to change as I became more and more intensely caught up in the many issues relating to our treatment of and relationship with animals. This culminated six years ago in the formation of our Zoo Check Charitable Trust which investigates captive conditions for wildlife and promotes conservation of the natural habitat.

As the weeks of research for this anthology continued — mainly in the Arts Council's marvellous Poetry Library on the South Bank — Anne and I found we were not alone in our concern. Centuries of poets have expressed bitterness, sorrow and anger about man's treatment of animals. It was fascinating to discover how many such poems had been written and they influenced our decision regarding the character of this book. Of course we have included writing that extols the beauty and wonder of wild animals, and the collection is not without humour, but we decided to try and present animals in a realistic way and steer clear of material that ridicules, sentimentalizes or humanizes them by, to use one example, dressing them up in clothes.

Sadly, through lack of space, many favourites have been excluded — among them D. H. Lawrence's *The Snake* and Blake's *Tiger, Tiger*, but these famous poems are to be found in other collections of poetry. Here you will find some familiar voices — and some unfamiliar ones as well — speaking with piercing clarity about the animal inhabitants of earth's beautiful but diminishing wildernesses. With equal poignancy you will also hear about those same creatures when they are subjected to man's whims in captivity.

Harsh the wild may be, but a wild life is what wild animals have evolved to live, and who are we to say it should be otherwise?

Virginia McKenna

Praise God for the animals,
for the colours of them,
for the stripes and spots of them,
for the patches and plains of them,
their claws and paws.

Lynn Warren

IN MEMORY OF
GEORGE ADAMSON
'LORD OF THE LIONS'

So they came
Grubbing, rooting, barking, sniffing,
Feeling for cold stars, for stone, for some hiding-place,
Loosed at last from heredity, able to eat
From any tree or from ground, merely mildly themselves,
And every movement was quick, was purposeful, was proposed.
The galaxies gazed on, drawing in their distances.
The beasts breathed out warm on the air.

No one had come to make anything of this,
To move it, name it, shape it a symbol;
The huge creatures were their own depth, the hills
Lived lofty there, wanting no climber.
Murmur of birds came, rumble of underground beasts
And the otter swam deftly over the broad river.

There was silence too.
Plants grew in it, it wove itself, it spread, it enveloped
The evening as day-calls died and the universe hushed, hushed.
A last bird flew, a first beast swam
And prey on prey
Released each other
(Nobody hunted at all):
They slept for the waiting day.

Elizabeth Jennings

from JUNGLE

Lions and tigers dominate
Headlines from the Jungle ...

Mary Carter Smith

PRIDE OF LIONS

They can swipe a tree dead with one paw,
Roar a jungle into a cold sweat
From tick to elephant; with one bite
They mincemeat whole bowels of buffalo.

After the banquet they yawn like kings,
Stretched in their long purple courts; the blaze
Of flesh burns down in their sceptred eyes;
They sleep, and unicorns pick their fangs.

We then, dreaming, draw them in the stars,
Paint them red on our banners, and wage
For their share of glory, with their rage,
Dressed in their skins, lion-hearted wars.

And we are cunning, can dig a pit,
Put them behind bars like lunatics,
Drug them to play bread-and-circus tricks
On children, or kill them with one shot.

So with our wits we usurp their thrones,
Pretend to be lionized in their pride
Of place, and, stigmatized with their blood,
Beard them in their holiest of dens.

Yet our familiar heraldry breeds
Only compassion, for, being blest
With might and mane, they dare to outlast
Us and all our arrogance of words.

Julian Ennis

THE CAPTIVE LION

Thou that in fury with thy knotted tail
Hast made this iron floor thy beaten drum;
That now in silence walks thy little space —
Like a sea-captain — careless what may come:

What power has brought your majesty to this,
Who gave those eyes their dull and sleepy look;
Who took their lightning out, and from thy throat
The thunder when the whole wide forest shook?

It was that man who went again, alone,
Into thy forest dark — Lord, he was brave!
That man a fly has killed, whose bones are left
Unburied till an earthquake digs his grave.

W. H. Davies

RIVERDALE LION

Bound lion, almost blind from meeting their gaze and popcorn,
the Saturday kids love you. It is their parents
who would paint your mane with polka-dots to match their
    California shirts
and would trim your nails for tie-clips.

Your few roars delight them. But they wish you would
    quicken your pace
and not disappear so often into your artificial cave
for there they think you partake of secret joys and race
through the jungle-green lair of memory
under an American sun as gold as your name.

But you fool them. You merely suffer the heat and scatter
    the flies
with your tail. You never saw Africa.
Your sign does not tell them that you were born here, in
    captivity,
you are as much a Canadian as they are.

John Robert Colombo

Next to the lion, the tiger is king of the jungle.
To him the animals bow their heads. They fear
his terrible anger, his swift relentless lunge.
In the moonless night his roar strikes the innocent ear
like thunder, like doom, like the world's end.
Proud he is of his powerful head, of his amber eyes,
proud of being a despot, a dictator, a jungle thug;
but sometimes, when he's not looking, his striped magnificence
ends up, spread-eagled on the floor, as a rug.

Virginia Graham

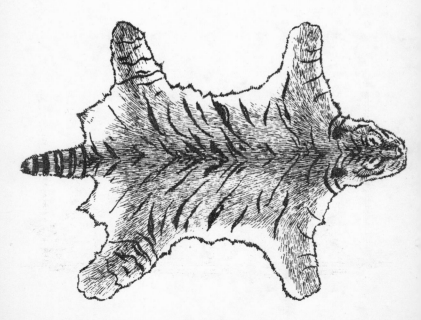

TIGER

Tiger, eyes dark with
half-remembered forest night,
stalks an empty cage.

Judith Nicholls

They hunt, the velvet tigers in the jungle,
The spotted jungle full of shapeless patches —
Sometimes they're leaves, sometimes they're hanging flowers,
Sometimes they're hot gold patches of the sun:
They hunt, the velvet tigers in the jungle!

What do they hunt by glimmering pools of water,
By the round silver Moon, the Pool of Heaven —
In the striped grass, amid the barkless trees —
The stars scattered like eyes of beasts above them!

What do they hunt, their hot breath scorching insects,
Insects that blunder blindly in the way,
Vividly fluttering — they also are hunting,
Are glittering with a tiny ecstasy!

The grass is flaming and the trees are growing,
The very mud is gurgling in the pools,
Green toads are watching, crimson parrots flying,
Two pairs of eyes meet one another glowing —
They hunt, the velvet tigers in the jungle.

W. J. Turner

The sun's no friend of mine, who grew up
around the glinting of moonlight on leaves.
All day I keep my eyes screwed tight
against the cascade of blood at my brain.
At night I come down from the trees.

No morality stalks my descent;
my logic is murder; I move on.
The dangling tail, the quiet shriek,
the fragile rustle of leaf on leaf,
the wildly staring eye:
these are offensive to me; that is all.
Memories distend my nostrils.

I am totally unexpected. I inhabit
the spaces of heights. The
moonlit deer, young boar, zebra
asleep in the grass: all
these are of prime interest to me;
these I make my business.

I am the nebulous footpad, man's
slow dance with death. I was there
just before you turned round. And
the catacombs, dark, wherein men retreat,
I constantly seek and gain access to them.

It is useless to keep me caged.
One day they will leave the gate out.
I am in constant readiness of this.
Parts of me never sleep.

Wayne Brown

Hushed, cruel, amber-eyed,
Before the time of the danger of the day,
Or at dusk on the boulder-broken mountainside
   The great cats seek their prey.

Soft-padded, heavy-limbed,
With agate talons chiselled for love or hate,
In desolate places wooded or granite-rimmed,
   The great cats seek their mate.

Rippling, as water swerved,
To tangled coverts overshadowed and deep
Or secret caves where the canyon's wall is curved,
    The great cats go for sleep.

    Seeking the mate or prey,
Out of the darkness glow the insatiate eyes.
Man, who is made more terrible far than they,
    Dreams he is otherwise!

George Sterling

NEVER GET OUT

I knew a little Serval cat —
   Never get out!
Would pad all day from this to that —
   Never get out!
From bar to bar she'd turn and turn,
   And in her eyes a fire would burn —
   (From her, Zoology we learn!)
   Never get out!

And if by hap a ray of sun
Came shining in her cage, she'd run
And sit upon her haunches, where
In the open she would stare,
And with the free that sunlight share —
   Never get out!

That catling's jungle heart forlorn
Will die as wild as it was born.
If I could cage the human race
Awhile, like her, in prisoned space,
And teach them what it is to face
   Never get out!

John Galsworthy

Birds are our angels — out of heaven
And in our heaven, making it.
How can the soul expect to rise
That steals the rapture from the skies
To abnegate and prison it?

I would go forth and cry aloud
The *liberty* of lovely birds.
I would inscribe on every cloud
That Love is God in rainbow words
But that my cries like theirs arise
On callous earth and careless skies.

Llywelyn

CAGED BIRD

A free bird leaps
on the back of the wind
and floats downstream
till the current ends
and dips his wing
in the orange sun rays
and dares to claim the sky.

But a bird that stalks
down his narrow cage
can seldom see through
his bars of rage
his wings are clipped and
his feet are tied
so he opens his throat to sing.

The caged bird sings
with a fearful trill
of things unknown
but longed for still
and his tune is heard
on the distant hill
for the caged bird
sings of freedom.

The free bird thinks of another breeze
and the trade winds soft through the sighing trees
and the fat worms waiting on a dawn-bright lawn
and he names the sky his own.

But a caged bird stands on the grave of dreams
his shadow shouts on a nightmare scream
his wings are clipped and his feet are tied
so he opens his throat to sing.

The caged bird sings
with a fearful trill
of things unknown
but longed for still
and his tune is heard
on the distant hill
for the caged bird
sings of freedom.

Maya Angelou

FLAMINGO

Not a word! not a word
Under the moon
When the glass of the blue lagoon
Is stirred,
And out of the reeds
In her scarlet weeds
   Steps the Flamingo.
A flame in flower,
A flower in flame,
As bright and brilliant
As her name,
   Princess Flamingo.
Radiant head!
Fantastic grace!
Delicate tread
That leaves no trace.
Before the moon
Sinks out of sight
She will take her flight
From the blue lagoon,
   Princess Flamingo.

Eleanor Farjeon

THE GIRAFFE

Hide of a leopard and hide of a deer
And eyes of a baby calf,
Sombre and large and crystal clear,
And a comical back that is almost sheer
Has the absurd giraffe.

A crane all covered with hide and hair
Is the aslant giraffe,
So cleverly mottled with many a square
That even the jungle is unaware
Whether a pair or a herd are there,
Or possibly one giraffe,
Or possibly only half.

If you saw him stoop and straddle and drink
He would certainly make you laugh,
He would certainly make you laugh, I think
With his head right down on the water's brink,
Would the invert giraffe,
The comical knock-kneed, angular, crock-kneed,
Anyhow-built giraffe.

There's more than a grain of common sense
And a husky lot of chaff
In the many and various arguments
About the first giraffe,
The first and worst giraffe;
Whether he grows a neck because
He yearned for the higher shoots
Out of the reach of all and each
Of the ruminating brutes;
Or whether he got to the shoots because
His neck was long, if long it was,
Is the cause of many disputes

Over the ladder without any rungs,
The stopper-like mouth and the longest of tongues
Of the rum and dumb giraffe,
The how-did-you-come giraffe,
The brown equatorial, semi-arboreal
Head-in-the-air giraffe.

Geoffrey Dearmer

THE GIRAFFE

For neck, a tulip-stalk;
Flower-head, far off and elegant;
Tongue, to fill your body's want
Stretched out like hands of a lady
Who takes her own naturally;
Wind netted in your small-paced walk;

Eyes dark and innocent;
Airy beast with flower's grace,
With bird's speed, with human face;
Painted like ground under trees
With light and shade; supple as these;
Horizon's instrument:

Strength flowers, speed, in you.
Speed is your soul's obedience.
Tiger and strolling wolf must dance
To other tunes, obeying God.
Strength is their fruit, who feed on blood;
But the trees kneel for you.

O meshed among high leaves,
Among clouds: I should never start
To see, when clouds or branches part,
Like a wild cherub's, bloom your head,
Serpent wise, dove feathers spread
Brushing the poplar's sleeves.

E. J. Scovell

THE GIRAFFE

The 2 f's
in giraffe
are like
2 giraffes
running through
the word giraffe

The 2 f's
run through giraffe
like 2 giraffes

Ron Padgett

IGUANA MEMORY

Saw an iguana once
when I was very small
in our backdam backyard
came rustling across my path

green like moving newleaf sunlight

big like big big lizard
with more legs than centipede
so it seemed to me
and it must have stopped a while
eyes meeting mine
iguana and child locked in a brief
split moment happening
before it went hurrying

for the green of its life

Grace Nichols

TO THE SNAKE

Green Snake, when I hung you round my neck
and stroked your cold, pulsing throat
   as you hissed to me, glinting
arrowy gold scales, and I felt
   the weight of you on my shoulders,
and the whispering silver of your dryness
   sounded close at my ears —

Green Snake — I swore to my companions that certainly
   you were harmless! But truly
I had no certainty, and no hope, only desiring
   to hold you, for that joy,
                which left
a long wake of pleasure, as the leaves moved
and you faded into the pattern
of grass and shadows, and I returned
smiling and haunted, to a dark morning.

Denise Levertov

A CROCODILE

Hard by the lilied Nile I saw
A duskish river-dragon stretched along,
The brown habergeon of his limbs enamelled
With sanguine almandines and rainy pearl:
And on his back there lay a young one sleeping,
No bigger than a mouse; with eyes like beads,
And a small fragment of its speckled egg
Remaining on its harmless, pulpy snout;
A thing to laugh at, as it gaped to catch
The baulking, merry flies. In the iron jaws
Of the great devil-beast, like a pale soul
Fluttering in rocky hell, lightsomely flew
A snowy trochilus, with roseate beak
Tearing the hairy leeches from his throat.

Thomas Lovell Beddoes

37

THE PARAKEETS

Across the fiery sandstone walls
The green tails of the parakeets
Make horizontal waterfalls
That vanish in the deep retreats
Where they assemble, school on school,
The casuarinas and the neems;
There still I catch their brilliant gleams;
Minute green suns that radiate cool.

Beside them, all the leafage pales
To dusty grey. They scream and shout,
Hanging and scrambling, with their tails,
Against the bark, spread fanwise out,
Yet when they flee again, they go
So sharp and straight and swift in flight
Those tails become green spines of light,
It seems the arrow speeds the bow.

The twilight skyline smoulders. But
Against that deepening glow they lack
All colour; wing to roost, and cut
Clear silhouettes of velvet black.
They made their greenness out of sun;
Although they seemed its counterpart,
Blazing against its blaze, at heart
Fact and counterpart were one.

John Holloway

ELEPHANTS

The world is full of Elephants,
The baby ones and taller ones.
African Elephants have great big ears,
The Indian ones have smaller ones.

Gavin Ewart

CIRCUS ELEPHANT

Does the Elephant remember
In the grey light before dawn,
Old noises of the jungle
In mornings long gone?

Does the Elephant remember
The cry of hungry beasts,
The Tiger and the Leopard,
The Lion at his feasts?

Do his mighty eardrums listen
For the thunder of the feet
Of the Buffalo and the Zebra
In the dark and dreadful heat?

Does His Majesty remember,
Does he stir himself and dream
Of the long-forgotten music
Of a long-forgotten dream?

Kathryn Worth

I wonder if the elephant
Is lonely in his stall
When all the boys and girls are gone
And there's no shout at all,
And there's no one to stamp before,
No one to note his might.
Does he hunch up, as I do,
Against the dark of night?

Gwendolyn Brooks

In my mind's eye – bird's eye –
I see the African plains.
Dry – huge – far as the eye of whatever kind
Can see.

Mountains on the edge of the sky
Stand violet – and inviolate –
Sentinels stretching to clouds.
Clouds forever changing the space pattern of blue.

Thornbush, acacia,
Umbrella pools of sanctuary and shade
In noon-day fire.
Grey coolness harbouring grey majesty
Of elephants.
Nature's monarchs.
                    Nature's great teachers.

Trunks curling and caressing,
Ears giant palm leaves,
Fanning,
To cool the noon-hot blood.
Wise eyes, lash-curtained,
High foreheads – noble.
Harbouring an ancient store of memories.

Flash of ivory amongst the grey.
Ivory-coloured prizes.
Coveted for carvings.
Unthroning mammoth kings and queens alike.
Returning all to dust.

My mind's eye weeps for you
As you fall to earth.
My small heart bleeds for yours
As your blood is spilled.

Red blood, splattering the earth
And thirst-racked thorns.
Scarlet on ivory –
Momentarily.
Then snatched away to light some vaulted store.
The ivory gleam has gone.
And darkness comes again to Africa.

Virginia McKenna

IN A CORNER OF EDEN

In a corner of Eden
the one-horned black
rare rhinoceros slept in the shade,
water among the reeds softly swam
yellow and green the ripening melons hang
softly slept.
In the hot light once
he went, stinking shade drops
dark over his head,
in Eden once
easy-bellied he lay
and breathed a gentle breath such as yellow
fruit or any sleeping beast may.

Peter Levi

Golden-winged, silver-winged,
   Winged with flashing flame,
Such a flight of birds I saw,
   Birds without a name:
Singing songs in their own tongue —
   Song of songs — they came.

One to another calling,
   Each answering each,
One to another calling
   In their proper speech:
High above my head they wheeled,
   Far out of reach.

On wings of flame they went and came
   With a cadenced clang:
Their silver wings tinkled,
   Their golden wings rang;
The wind it whistled through their wings
   Where in heaven they sang.

They flashed and they darted
　　Awhile before mine eyes,
Mounting, mounting, mounting still,
　　In haste to scale the skies,
Birds without a nest on earth,
　　Birds of Paradise.

Christina Rossetti

The Hamadryas Baboon at the Lincoln Park Zoo
Has gone crazy
In the silence beyond the glass boundary he bangs
His head
And under his elegant shouldercloak he bites
His foot
Now he is still, considering the wall from the porch
Of his eyes

The Hamadryas is a sacred Egyptian
These keepers have Fury locked up here

Edward Dorn

What culture will this ape-child inherit
In his white hygienic age? His mother
Shields him with a tender arm, she eats
His afterbirth; and he relaxes, held
To her enormous hairy breast, and is
Briefly and dreamlessly at rest, closing
Such babyish ancient anxious wrinkled eyes.

Watch his huge male parent next, watch
His weary muscular four-legged walk
To nothing at all across his white hygienic
Cage. Watch his immense felted thighs, when his
Ancient apishness is smudged, and slowly,
Dully, his leafaged dream of ape-life dies.

Geoffrey Grigson

At eight o'clock in the evening
   And at two in the afternoon,
The monster curtain opens,
   The fiddles creak and croon,
And then I bow to the people,
   A lumbering baboon.

I wonder why I do it?
   Why do the humans stare
From even rows of shadow
   Behind the footlights' glare?
Why do I go through my weary tricks
   On a table and a chair?

They laugh and clap and giggle,
   They never seem to tire,
For I am quite amusing
   As I dance upon a wire,
Or leap, at my master's signal,
   Through golden hoops of fire.

I cannot smile, like the people,
    I cannot speak at all;
I pirouette insanely
    In the foolish carnival;
Yet could I laugh, O, I would laugh
    When the velvet curtains fall!

For I wonder why those people
    Sit in such even rows,
And smile at my useless knowledge,
    Laugh at my mincing toes,
And dream that they have wisdom! —
    How little a human knows!

C. H. Towne

On Sunday, all come to the zoo.
Zipped in my ape-suit tight, I freak
public. When a child tosses a
peanut through, I eat it like you.

This is a zoo. And who are you?
Outside my cage, sane citizens
lime on stilts in their Sunday-suits.
Slinging in fruit, they make me do

an insane rock-steady for you;
make me stand on my head and do
other tricks to almost prove right
my wrong-presence here in this zoo

This is a cage. And who are you?
Two neighbouring lions, half-seen
through slits, recline in the sun.
They hate everything human; will do

not even the least trick for you.
Their common contempt makes us one.
I pitch back your fruit. When you trip
on my skin of sickness, bruised blue,

I'll slip from my cage, and into
the pure life of lions. I am death-
sick of being two. These sane green
animals seal my rent like glue.

On Sunday, all come to the zoo.
Zipped out, it's easy to freak in
from you. But, conversely, right on
cue, the others do tricks for you.

Tony McNeill

MONKEYS

Two little creatures
With faces the size of
A pair of pennies
Are clasping each other.
'Ah, do not leave me,'
One says to the other,
In the high monkey-
Cage in the beast-shop.

There are no people
To gape at them now,
For people are loth to
Peer in the dimness;
Have they not builded
Streets and playhouses,
Sky-signs and bars,
To lose the loneliness
Shaking the hearts
Of the two little Monkeys?

Yes. But who watches
The penny-small faces
Can hear the voices:
'Ah, do not leave me;
Suck I will give you,
Warmth and clasping,
And if you slip from
This beam I can never
Find you again.'

Dim is the evening,
And chill is the weather;
There, drawn from their coloured
Hemisphere,
The apes lilliputian
With faces the size of
A pair of pennies,
And voices as low as
The flow of my blood.

Padraic Colum

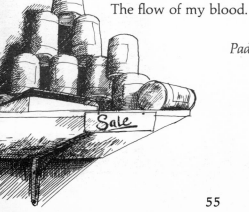

The gorilla lay on his back,
One hand cupped under his head,
Like a man.

Like a labouring man tired with work,
A strong man with his strength burnt away
In the toil of earning a living.

Only of course he was not tired out with work,
Merely with boredom; his terrible strength
All burnt away by prodigal idleness.

A thousand days, and then a thousand days,
Idleness licked away his beautiful strength
He having no need to earn a living.

It was all laid on, free of charge.
We maintained him, not for doing anything,
But for being what he was.

And so that Sunday morning he lay on his back,
Like a man, like a worn-out man,
One hand cupped under his terrible hard head.

Like a man, like a man,
One of those we maintain, not for doing anything,
But for being what they are.

A thousand days, and then a thousand days,
With everything laid on, free of charge,
They cup their heads in prodigal idleness.

John Wain

A CAMEL

In thin shade
a camel that is fastened,
like an aged man,
mumbling and mumbling, is eating things all day long.
His tent is like a sky with snow,
hanging grey and dismal.
Without speaking the camel
keeps moving his mouth all day.

Sasei Murō
transl. E. M. Shiffert and Yuki Sawa

THE DROMEDARY

In dreams I see the Dromedary still,
  As once in a gay park I saw him stand:
  A thousand eyes in vulgar wonder scanned
His humps and hairy neck, and gazed their fill
At his lank shanks and mocked with laughter shrill.
  He never moved: and if his Eastern land
  Flashed on his eye with stretches of hot sand,
It wrung no mute appeal from his proud will.
He blinked upon the rabble lazily;
  And still some trace of majesty forlorn
And a coarse grace remained: his head was high,
  Though his gaunt flanks with a great mange were worn:
There was not any yearning in his eye,
  But on his lips and nostril infinite scorn.

A. Y. Campbell

What do you think of me?
I have a rough coat like Africa.
I am crafty with dark spots
like the bush-tufted plains of Africa.
I sprawl as a shaggy bundle of gathered energy
like Africa sprawling in its waters.
I trot, I lope, I slaver, I am a ranger.
I hunch my shoulders. I eat the dead.

Do you like my song?
When the moon pours hard and cold on the veldt
I sing, and I am the slave of darkness.
Over the stone walls and the mud walls and the ruined places
and the owls, the moonlight falls.
I sniff a broken drum. I bristle. My pelt is silver.
I howl my song to the moon — up it goes.
Would you meet me there in the waste places?

It is said I am a good match
for a dead lion. I put my muzzle
at his golden flanks, and tear. He
is my golden supper, but my tastes are easy.
I have a crowd of fangs, and I use them.
Oh and my tongue – do you like me
when it comes lolling out over my jaw
very long, and I am laughing?
I am not laughing.
But I am not snarling either, only
panting in the sun, showing you
what I grip
carrion with.

I am waiting
for the foot to slide,
for the heart to seize,
for the leaping sinews to go slack,
for the fight to the death to be fought to the death,
for a glazing eye and the rumour of blood.
I am crouching in my dry shadows
till you are ready for me.
My place is to pick you clean
and leave your bones to the wind.

Edwin Morgan

THE ZEBRA

The zebra is undoubtedly
a source of some confusion,
his alternating stripes present
an optical illusion.

Observing them is difficult,
one quickly loses track
of whether they are black on white
or rather, white on black.

Jack Prelutsky

ZEBRA

White men in Africa,
Puffing at their pipes,
Think the zebra's a white horse
With black stripes.

Black men in Africa,
With pipes of different types,
Know the Zebra's a black horse
With white stripes.

Gavin Ewart

From the dark woods that breathe of fallen showers,
Harnessed with level rays in golden reins,
The zebras draw the dawn across the plains
Wading knee-deep among the scarlet flowers.
The sunlight, zithering their flanks with fire,
Flashes between the shadows as they pass
Barred with electric tremors through the grass
Like wind along the gold strings of a lyre.

Into the flushed air snorting rosy plumes
That smoulder round their feet in drifting fumes,
With dove-like voices call the distant fillies,
While round the herds the stallion wheels his flight,
Engine of beauty volted with delight,
To roll his mare among the trampled lilies.

Roy Campbell

FROM THE SHORE

A lone gray bird,
Dim-dipping, far-flying,
Alone in the shadows and grandeurs and tumults
Of night and the sea
And the stars and storms.

Out over the darkness it wavers and hovers,
Out into the gloom it swings and batters,
Out into the wind and the rain and the vast,
Out into the pit of a great black world,
Where fogs are at battle, sky-driven, sea-blown,
Love of mist and rapture of flight,
Glories of chance and hazards of death
On its eager and palpitant wings.

Out into the deep of the great dark world,
Beyond the long borders where foam and drift
Of the sundering waves are lost and gone
On the tides that plunge and rear and crumble.

Carl Sandburg

THE SONG OF THE WHALE

Heaving mountain in the sea,
Whale, I heard you
Grieving.

Great whale, crying for your life,
Crying for your kind, I knew
How we would use
Your dying:

Lipstick for our painted faces,
Polish for our shoes.

Tumbling mountain in the sea,
Whale, I heard you
Calling.

Bird-high notes, keening,
soaring:
At their edge a tiny drum
Like a heartbeat.

We would make you
Dumb.

In the forest of the sea,
Whale, I heard you
Singing,

Singing to your kind.
We'll never let you be.
Instead of life we choose

Lipstick for our painted faces,
Polish for our shoes.

Kit Wright

There Leviathan
Hugest of living creatures, on the deep
Stretched like a promontory, sleeps or swims,
And seems a moving land, and at his gills
Draws in, and at his trunk spouts out, a sea.

John Milton

DEATH OF A WHALE

When the mouse died, there was a sort of pity;
The tiny, delicate creature made for grief,
Yesterday, instead, the dead whale on the reef
Drew an excited multitude to the jetty.
How must a whale die to wring a tear?
Lugubrious death of a whale; the big
Feast for the gulls and sharks; the tug
Of the tide simulating life still there,
Until the air, polluted, swings this way
Like a door ajar from a slaughterhouse.
Pooh! Pooh! spare us, give us the death of a mouse
By its tiny hole; not this in our lovely bay.
– Sorry, we are, too, when a child dies:
But at the immolation of a race, who cries?

John Blight

DOLPHINS

for Tom Durham

They've brains the size of a man's and they like music –
surely make it ... May be exchanging speech?

    We (it seems) catch their low
notes only –
     and they, of human music,
     may read more than we know –
firm shapes, shot with elusive depths, of dapples
subtly disturbed by thrusts of arabesque,
     the way a floor mosaic
     mixes its own clear message
in with the high riches, the dappled panels.

Do dolphins stop just short of words? talk music?
Having preferred purity, think in music?

Jonathan Griffin

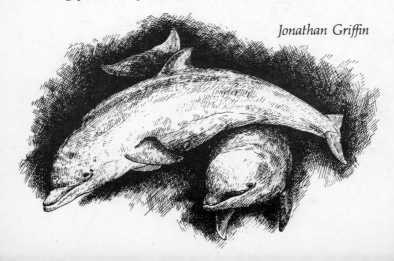

SEAL LULLABY

Oh! hush thee, my baby, the night is behind us,
And black are the waters that sparkled so green.
The moon, o'er the combers, looks downward to find us
At rest in the hollows that rustle between.
Where billow meets billow, there soft be thy pillow;
Ah, weary wee flipperling, curl at thy ease!
The storm shall not wake thee, nor sharks overtake thee,
Asleep in the arms of the slow-swinging seas.

Rudyard Kipling

A SOUVENIR

On my Auntie Mabel's mantelpiece
There sits a seal. Not live and real
Of course, but tiny, dead and real.
Know what I mean? It's made of seal;
Dead thing, but true to life in each detail.

I wonder how a seal must think
(If think it can) or feel at brink
Of sea to hear the culling call
Of man to man as men wade in
To beat with staves this solid flesh
(Still frail) to make a souvenir of Canada
That sits on Auntie Mabel's mantelpiece.

John Kitching

Take not away the life you cannot give,
For all things have an equal right to live.

John Dryden

POLAR BEAR

Hugging the wall, down
there in his open pit,
he ambles absently,
fitting his whole body
to the wide curve
of dingy cement.

Backwards and forwards
loping, big head weaving,
pressing one matted flank
and then the other
to the sun-scorched cliff
of his lonely prison.

His coat is far
from white — rather
a drab cream, with
yellow or brownish stains.
— He looks unhappy in the heat.
No wonder he never

turns to growl at
us, begging for attention.

James Kirkup

I saw two Bears, as white as any milk,
Lying together in a mighty cave,
Of mild aspect, and hair as soft as silk,
That savage nature seemed not to have,
Nor after greedy spoil of blood to crave;
Two fairer beasts might not elsewhere be found,
Although the compassed world were sought around.
But what can long abide above this ground
In state of bliss, or steadfast happiness?

Edmund Spenser

Stranger in his own element,
Sea-casualty, the castaway manikin
Waddles in his tailored coat-tails. Oil

Has spread a deep commercial stain
Over his downy shirtfront. Sleazy, grey,
It clogs the sleekness. Far too well

He must recall the past, to be so cautious:
Watch him step into the waves. He shudders
Under the froth, slides, slips, on the wet sand,

Escaping to dryness, dearth, in a white cascade,
An involuntary shouldering off of gleam.
Hands push him back into the sea. He stands

In pained and silent expostulation.
Once he knew a sunlit, leaping smoothness,
But close within his head's small knoll, and dark

He retains the image: oil on sea,
Green slicks, black lassos of sludge
Sleaving the breakers in a stain-spread scarf.

He shudders now from the clean flinching wave,
Turns and plods back up the yellow sand,
Ineffably weary, triumphantly sad.

He is immensely wise: he trusts nobody. His senses
Are clogged with experience. He eats
Fish from his Saviour's hands, and it tastes black.

Ruth Miller

THE ARCTIC FOX

No feet. Snow.
Ear — a star-cut
Crystal of silence.
The world hangs watched.

Jaws flimsy as ice
Champ at the hoar-frost
Of something tasteless —
A snowflake of feathers.

The forest sighs.
A fur of breath
Empty as moonlight
Has a blue shadow.

A dream twitches
The sleeping face
Of the snow-lit land.

When day wakes
Sun will not find
What night hardly noticed.

Ted Hughes

THE OWL

The owl hooted and told of
   the morning star,
He hooted again and told of
   the dawn.

Hopi Indians,
North America

A NIGHT WITH A WOLF

High up on the lonely mountains,
   Where the wild men watched and waited;
Wolves in the forest, and bears in the bush,
   And I on my path belated.

The rain and the night together
   Came down, and the wind came after,
Bending the props of the pine-tree roof,
   And snapping many a rafter.

I crept along in the darkness,
   Stunned, and bruised, and blinded;
Crept to a fir with thick-set boughs,
   And a sheltering rock behind it.

There, from the blowing and raining,
    Crouching, I sought to hide me.
Something rustled; two green eyes shone;
    And a wolf lay down beside me!

His wet fur pressed against me;
    Each of us warmed the other;
Each of us felt, in the stormy dark,
    That beast and man were brother.

And when the falling forest
    No longer crashed in warning,
Each of us went from our hiding place
    Forth in the wild, wet morning.

Bayard Taylor

still on his lone rock
stares at the uncaged stars and
cries into the night.

Judith Nicholls

—— THE DALLIANCE OF THE EAGLES ——

Skirting the river road, (my forenoon walk, my rest,)
Skyward in air a sudden muffled sound, the dalliance of the
    eagles,
The rushing amorous contact high in space together,
The clinching interlocking claws, a living, fierce, gyrating
    wheel,
Four beating wings, two beaks, a swirling mass tight
    grappling,
In tumbling, turning clustering loops, straight downward
    falling,
Till o'er the river pois'd, the twain yet one, a moment's lull,
A motionless still balance in the air, then parting, talons,
    loosing,
Upward again on slow-firm pinions slanting, their separate
    diverse flight,
She hers, he his, pursuing.

Walt Whitman

'Bless the child!
Eagle! why, you know nought of eagles, you.
When we lay off the coast, Canada way,
And chanced to be ashore when twilight fell,
That was the place for eagles; bald they were,
With eyes as yellow as gold.'
'O, Martin, dear,
Tell me about them.'
'Tell! there's nought to tell,
Only they snored o' nights and frighted us.'
'Snored?'
'Aye, I tell you, snored; they slept upright
In the great oaks by scores; as true as time,
If I'd had aught upon my mind just then,
I wouldn't have walked that wood for unknown gold;
It was most awful. When the moon was full,
I've seen them fish at night, in the middle watch,
When she got low. I've seen them plunge like stones,
And come up fighting with a fish as long,
Ay, longer than my arm; and they would sail –
When they had struck its life out – they would sail
Over the deck, and show their fell, fierce eyes,
And croon for pleasure, hug the prey, and speed
Grand as a frigate on a wind.'

Jean Ingelow

—— COYOTE, OR THE PRAIRIE WOLF ——

Blown out of the prairie in twilight and dew,
Half bold and half timid, yet lazy all through,
Loth ever to leave, and yet fearful to stay,
He limps in the clearing, — an outcast in grey.

A shade on the stubble, a ghost by the wall,
Now leaping, now limping, now risking a fall,
Lop-eared and large jointed, but ever alway
A thoroughly vagabond outcast in grey.

Here, Carlo, old fellow, he's one of your kind, —
Go seek him, and bring him in out of the wind.
What! snarling, my Carlo! So — even dogs may
Deny their own kin in the outcast in grey!

Well, take what you will, — though it be on the sly,
Marauding or begging, — I shall not ask why;
But will call it a dole, just to help on his way
A four-footed friar in orders of grey!

Bret Harte

—— THE FLOWER-FED BUFFALOES ——

The flower-fed buffaloes of the spring
In the days of long ago,
Ranged where the locomotives sing
And the prairie flowers lie low: —
The tossing, blooming, perfumed grass
Is swept away by the wheat,
Wheels and wheels and wheels spin by
In the spring that still is sweet.
But the flower-fed buffaloes of the spring
Left us, long ago.
They gore no more, they bellow no more,
They trundle around the hills no more: —
With the Blackfeet, lying low,
With the Pawnees, lying low,
Lying low.

Vachel Lindsay

88

BUFFALO DUSK

The buffaloes are gone.
And those who saw the buffaloes are gone.
Those who saw the buffaloes by thousands and how they
      pawed the prairie sod into dust with their hoofs, their
      great heads down pawing on in a great pageant of
      dusk,
Those who saw the buffaloes are gone.
And the buffaloes are gone.

Carl Sandburg

HUMMING-BIRD

I can imagine, in some otherworld
Primeval-dumb, far back
In that most awful stillness, that only gasped and hummed,
Humming-birds raced down the avenues.

Before anything had a soul,
While life was a heave of Matter, half inanimate,
This little bit chipped off in brilliance
And went whizzing through the slow, vast, succulent stems.

I believe there were no flowers then,
In the world where the humming-bird flashed ahead of
        creation.
I believe he pierced the slow vegetable veins with his long
        beak.

Probably he was big
As mosses, and little lizards, they say, were once big.
Probably he was a jabbing, terrifying monster.

We look at him through the wrong end of the long
        telescope of Time,
Luckily for us.

D. H. Lawrence

from KANGAROO

Delicate mother Kangaroo
Sitting up there rabbit-wise, but huge, plumb-weighted,
And lifting her beautiful slender face, oh! so much more
    gently and finely lined than a rabbit's, or than a hare's,
Lifting her face to nibble at a round white peppermint
    drop, which she loves, sensitive mother Kangaroo.

Her sensitive, long, pure-bred face.
Her full antipodal eyes, so dark,
So big and quiet and remote, having watched so many
    empty dawns in silent Australia.

Her little loose hands, and drooping Victorian shoulders.
And then her great weight below the waist, her vast pale belly
With a thin young yellow little paw hanging out, and
    straggle of a long thin ear, like ribbon,
Like a funny trimming to the middle of her belly, thin
    little dangle of an immature paw, and one thin ear ...

D. H. Lawrence

THE BELL-BIRD

The stillness of the Austral noon
Is broken by no single sound –
No lizards even on the ground
Rustle amongst dry leaves – no tune
The lyre-bird sings – yet hush! I hear
A soft bell tolling, silvery clear!
    Low soft aerial chimes, unknown
    Save 'mid these silences alone.

William Sharp

THE PARROT

Within her gilded cage confined,
I saw a dazzling Belle,
A Parrot of that famous kind
Whose name is NON-PAREIL.

Like beads of glossy jet her eyes;
And, smoothed by Nature's skill,
With pearl or gleaming agate vies
Her finely-curvèd bill.

Her plumy mantle's living hues
In mass opposed to mass,
Outshine the splendour that imbues
The robes of pictured glass.

And, sooth to say, an apter Mate
Did never tempt the choice
Of feathered Thing most delicate
In figure and in voice.

But, exiled from Australian bowers,
And singleness her lot,
She trills her song with tutored powers,
Or mocks each casual note.

No more of pity for regrets
With which she may have striven!
Now but in wantonness she frets,
Or spite, if cause be given;

Arch, volatile, a sportive bird
By social glee inspired;
Ambitious to be seen or heard,
And pleased to be admired!

William Wordsworth

BEI-SHUNG

I am *Bei-shung*, they call me the white bear.
I am the hidden king of these bamboo forests,
Invisible with my white fur and my black fur
Among this snow, these dark rocks and shadows.

I am the hidden king of these mountain heights,
Not a clown, not a toy. I do not care
To be seen. I walk, for all my weight,
Like a ghost on the soles of my black feet.

Invisible with my black fur and my white fur
I haunt the streams. I flip out little fishes;
I scoop them out of the water with my hand.
(I have a thumb, like you. I have a hand.)

Among this sparkling snow, these rocks and shadows,
I roam. Time is my own. My teeth are massive.
My jaw is a powerful grinder. I feed
On chewy bamboo, on small creatures, fish, birds.

You call me Panda. I am King *Bei-shung*.

Gerard Benson

Grandfather, Grandfather,
what do pandas say?
Grandfather, Grandfather,
as among the rocks they roll
and rather sadly play
a game that seems
to do with dreams
of places far away.
Grandfather, Grandfather,
what do pandas say?

Grand-daughter, Grand-daughter,
when the pandas play
rather sadly in the rocks
this is what they say
to one another as they seem
to remember in a dream
those places far away:
'Let us tell no one
the word that we say
softly to one another

as we roll and play.
For if they ever heard it,
the tall two-legged Understanders
who always want to know what pandas
like us love to say,
yes, if they ever heard it
they would take it away.'

George Barker

—ON WATCHING THE BEARS IN THE — BEARPITS AT BERNE

Here's your audience, Lady Grizzle;
Rise up on your massive great feet.
The public are crowding the railings
And it's you they are waiting to meet.
That little boy's throwing a carrot,
So open your mouth, clever bear!
You are here to amuse with such antics
As would make your wild relatives stare.

Lie on your back, gentle Friska;
You too have a favourite trick.
Catch the figs in your paws as you lie there —
What matter if they make you sick?
What do you know of the mountains?
Life is bounded for you by a pit.
Your role is to give entertainment,
It's your duty to 'Beg! Dance and Sit!'

In the nursery pit cubs are playing,
With a juvenile lack of concern.
As far as they know, life's all pleasure.
After all, they're the mascots of Berne.
Captivity's all they've encountered;
Does any world outside exist?
Can they really feel sorrow or yearning
For the life in the wild that they've missed?

Margaret Porter

'Twould ring the bells of Heaven
The wildest peals for years,
If Parson lost his senses
And people came to theirs,
And he and they together
Knelt down with angry prayers
For tamed and shabby tigers,
And dancing dogs and bears ...

Ralph Hodgson

——— THE BEAR ON THE DELHI ROAD ———

Unreal   tall as a myth
by the road the Himalayan bear
is beating the brilliant air
with his crooked arms
About him two men   bare
spindly as locusts   leap

One pulls on a ring
in the great soft nose   His mate
flicks   flicks with a stick
up at the rolling eyes

They have not led him here
down from the fabulous hills
to this bald alien plain
and the clamorous world   to kill
but simply to teach him to dance

They are peaceful both   these spare
men of Kashmir   and the bear
alive is their living   too
If   far on the Delhi way
around him galvanic they dance
it is merely to wear   wear
from his shaggy body the tranced
wish forever to stay
only an ambling bear
four-footed in berries

It is no more joyous for them
in this hot dust to prance
out of reach of the praying claws
sharpened to paw for ants
in the shadows of deodars

It is not easy to free
myth from reality
or rear this fellow up
to lurch   lurch with them
in the tranced dancing of men

Earle Birney

THE TRAVELLING BEAR

Grass-blades push up between the cobblestones
And catch the sun on their flat sides
Shooting it back,
Gold and emerald,
Into the eyes of passers-by.

And over the cobblestones,
Square-footed and heavy,
Dances the trained bear.
The cobbles cut his feet,
And he has a ring in his nose
Which hurts him;
But still he dances,
For the keeper pricks him with a sharp stick,
Under his fur.

Now the crowd gapes and chuckles,
And boys and young women shuffle their feet in time
    to the dancing bear.
They see him wobbling
Against a dust of emerald and gold,
And they are greatly delighted.

The legs of the bear shake with fatigue,
And his back aches,
And the shining grass-blades dazzle and confuse him.
But still he dances.
Because of the little, pointed stick.

Amy Lowell

What hath this creature done that he should be
Thus beaten, wounded and tired out by me?
He is my fellow-creature.

John Flavell

Some with cruelty came, sharp-fanged and clawed,
Tore at the air searching for food which, found,
They ate in an instant — new leaves, the tall and small
Flowers. Carnivores were
Worse, hunters of blood, smellers of victims
More miles away than our instruments measure or we
Imagine. Meanwhile the jungle listened and looked.
The parrot kept its beak shut, the slithering snake
Stilled to a coil. The stars were listening, the sun's
Burning paused at the tear and rampage of
A striped or spotted creature. This was the time
Before we were.

Now we have caged and enclosed but not enchanted
Most of these. Now full of power we are not
Gentle with flowers, pull too hard, break the admired
Rose with abandonment. We should know better.

You have heard of the ark and Noah. Most likely it
Was a local event or a myth but remember men
Bow down to the myths they create.
Perhaps we were kindest, most gentle,
Most at our best
When we coupled all creatures and launched them forth in an ark.
Imagination was gracious then indeed,
Gracious too when we thought up the speeding dove,
Feathery emblem of peace whiter than clouds, its wings
Combing and calming the breakers. The waters stilled.

You have heard now of some of these, learnt of their habits.
Do not haunt zoos too often, do not demand
Affection too often from rabbits or cats or dogs,
Do not tame if taming hurts.
Be grateful for such variety of manners,
For the diverse universe.
Above all respect the smallest of all these creatures
As you are awed by the stars.

Elizabeth Jennings

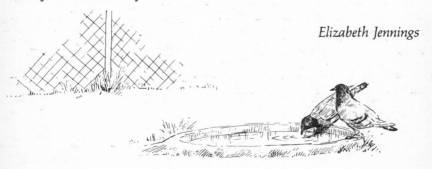

ACKNOWLEDGEMENTS

The editor and publishers gratefully acknowledge permission to reproduce copyright poems in this book:

Virago Press for 'Caged Bird' by Maya Angelou, reprinted from *And Still I Rise*, copyright © Maya Angelou, 1986; Faber & Faber, Ltd for 'Grandfather, Grandfather' by George Barker, reprinted from *To Aylsham Fair*, copyright © George Barker, 1973; Gerard Benson for 'Beishung', copyright © Gerard Benson, 1990; McClelland and Stewart, Toronto for 'The Bear on the Delhi Road' by Earle Birney, from *Collected Poems*, copyright © Earle Birney, 1966; Angus and Robertson for 'Death of a Whale' by John Blight reprinted from *Beachcombers Diary*, copyright © John Blight, 1965; The David Company, Chicago for 'Pete at the Zoo' by Gwendolyn Brooks from *Blacks*, copyright © Gwendolyn Brooks, 1987; Hamish Hamilton for 'Tiger' by Wayne Brown, reprinted from *Breaklight* edited by Andrew Salkey, copyright © Wayne Brown, 1968; McClelland and Stewart, Toronto for 'Riverdale Lion' by John Robert Colombo from *Abracadabra*, copyright © John Robert Colombo, 1967; The Estate of Padraic Colum for 'Monkeys' by Padraic Colum, reprinted from *Collected Poems* published by Macmillan, US, copyright © The Estate of Padraic Colum; Jonathan Cape for 'The Captive Lion' by W. H. Davies, reprinted from *Collected Poems*, copyright © the Executors of the W. H. Davies Estate, 1934; Geoffrey Dearmer for 'The Giraffe' by Geoffrey Dearmer, reprinted from *Book Four Round the World Poetry*, copyright © Geoffrey Dearmer; Four Seasons Publishing for 'Heavy Acquisition' by Edward Dorn, reprinted from *Collected Poems*, copyright © Edward Dorn, 1975, 1983; Julian Ennis for 'Pride of Lions', copyright © Julian Ennis, 1990; Century Hutchinson Ltd for 'Zebra' and 'Elephants' by Gavin Ewart, reprinted from *The Learned Hippopotamus*, copyright © Gavin Ewart, 1987; David Higham for 'Flamingo' by Eleanor Farjeon, reprinted from *Silver-Sand and Snow* published by Michael Joseph, copyright © Eleanor Farjeon, 1951; Virginia Thesiger for 'T for Tiger', copyright © Virginia Graham, 1989; Jonathan Griffin for 'Dolphins', copyright © Jonathan Griffin, 1990; Secker & Warburg for 'In the Zoo' by Geoffrey Grigson reprinted from *Montaigne's Tower and Other Poems*, copyright © Geoffrey Grigson; Mrs Hodgson and Macmillan for 'from The Bells of Heaven' by Ralph Hodgson, reprinted from *Collected Poems*, copyright © Ralph Hodgson, 1961; David Higham for 'The Parakeets' by John Holloway reprinted from *The Fugue* published by Routledge, copyright © John Holloway, 1961; Faber & Faber, Ltd for 'The Arctic Fox' by Ted Hughes, reprinted from *Under the North Star* by Ted Hughes, copyright © Ted Hughes, 1981; David Higham for 'The Animals' Arrival' by Elizabeth Jennings, reprinted from *The Animals' Arrival* published by Macmillan, copyright © Elizabeth Jennings, 1969; David Higham for 'Finale for the Animals' by Elizabeth Jennings, reprinted from *Collected Poems*, published by Macmillan, copyright © Elizabeth Jennings, 1978; James Kirkup for 'Polar Bear', reprinted from *New Angels 1*, edited by John Foster, published by Oxford University Press, copyright © James Kirkup, 1987; John Kitching for 'A Souvenir' by John Kitching, reprinted from *Second Poetry Book* edited by John Foster published by Oxford University Press, copyright © John Kitching,

**Heaving mountain in the sea,
Whale, I heard you
Grieving...**

Look deep inside the animal world today and what
will you find? This compelling collection of poems
shows a diverse, mysterious and wonderful world
faced with danger, exploitation and extinction.
It's unforgettable poetry with an unforgettable
insight.

'A rich and varied collection' – *Guardian*

'Beautifully presented'
– *The Times Educational Supplement*

Cover and illustrations by Tessa Lovatt-Smith

 **A PUFFIN BOOK**

ISBN 0-14-034214-1

90101

U.K.   £2.99
CAN. $5.99

9 780140 342147